Piano
Grade 7

Pieces & Exercises
for Trinity College London exams

2015-2017

Published by
Trinity College London
www.trinitycollege.com
Registered in the UK
Company no. 02683033
Charity no. 1014792

Sonata in D

K.512; L.339

Domenico Scarlatti
(1685-1757)

3

Allegretto

Second movement from Sonata in F, op. 4 no. 6

Muzio Clementi
(1752-1832)

10

[Blank page to facilitate page turns]

Sicilienne

Arranged by S Dushkin

Maria-Theresia v Paradis
(1759-1824)

Adam's Allemande

from *An Album for my Friends*

Edward Gregson
(born 1945)

Presto

First movement from Sonata in A

Thomas Augustine Arne
(1710-1778)

Trills may be played as acciaccaturas (except in bar 18)

Improvisation

from *Pièces brèves pour piano*

Gabriel Fauré
(1845-1924)

Petites litanies de Jésus

from *L'Almanach aux images*

Gabriel Grovlez
(1879-1944)

Struttin' at the Waldorf *

no. 3 of Three Little Bites at the Big Apple

Philip Lane
(born 1950)

* A picture of Fred Astaire gliding through the lobby of the
New York hotel around 1935, in top hat, white tie and tails.

(imaginary tap dance steps)

* Players with smaller hands may omit the lower C.

At Miss Florence's

(homage to Robert Schumann)

David Earl
(born 1951)

Exercises

1a. Aria Semplice – tone, balance and voicing

1b. Forlorn Forlane – tone, balance and voicing

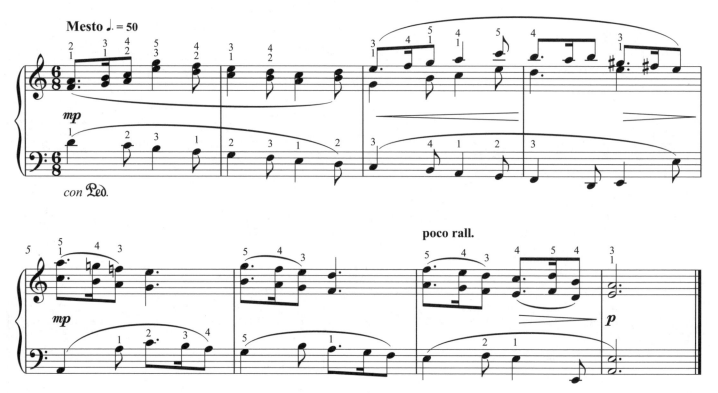

2a. Sad Song – co-ordination

2b. A Touch of 'Roque – co-ordination

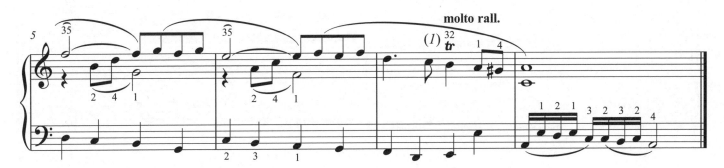

3a. Ever So Slightly Dizzy – finger & wrist strength and flexibility

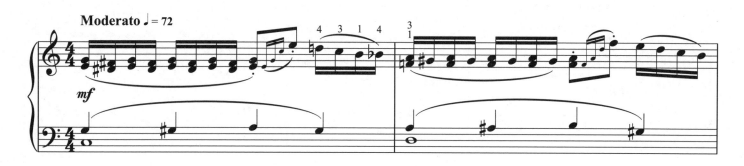

3b. Rustling Leaves – finger & wrist strength and flexibility

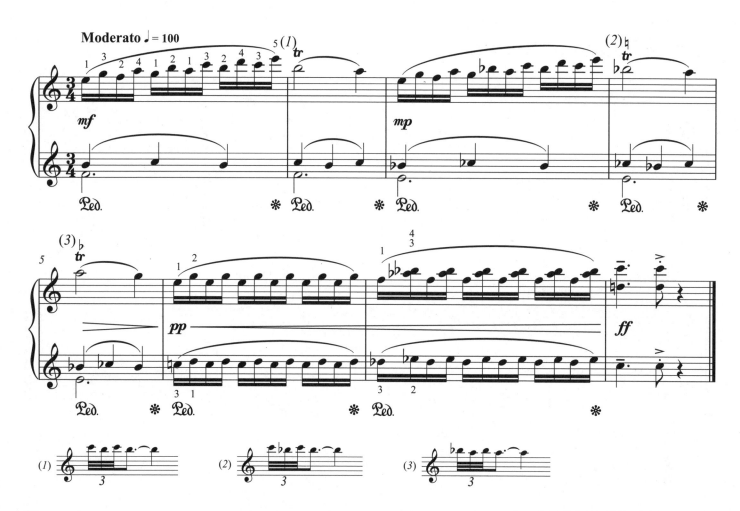